Mandala Salad

Gluten-free recipes and simple practices to
nourish the body and satisfy the spirit

Dr. April J. Modesti, D.C.

with Susan E. Schwartz

Mandala Salad:

Gluten-free recipes and simple practices to nourish the body and satisfy the spirit

by Dr. April J. Modesti and Susan E. Schwartz

Published by:
Serenity Press
1180 Los Altos Avenue
Los Altos, CA 94022

ISBN 978-0615633091

First printing 2012

Printed and bound in the United States of America

May this bring health, well-being, and deliciousness into your life! - A.J.M.
To my mother, who tried to teach me the right way to eat. - S.E.S.

When we open up our consciousness
and dwell in the beauty of Nature,
we allow healing to enter our lives.

- Bernard Jensen, Ph.D, Food Healing for Man

Photo by Susanne von Schroeder

Table of Contents

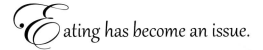ating has become an issue.

We are too busy to eat. We don't know what to eat. Or we've developed sensitivities that keep us from eating what we want.

And yet, there is nothing more fundamental to our health and well-being than what and how we eat.

My intention in writing this book is to suggest several different ways in which you can reacquaint yourself, or discover for the first time, extraordinary pleasures, health and spiritual connection in conscious eating.

I present a range of ideas of how to bring awareness and appreciation to your table, even if you are extremely busy. If you are gluten sensitive, the recipes included here will show you how you can eat gluten free with extraordinary pleasure. The ingredients are simple. The results are sublime!

Whether you have food challenges, are curious about the connection between food and spirituality or are looking for first steps on the path to more healthful eating, you will find nourishment here.

Sit down. Sample what calls to you.

Eat. Enjoy.

Photo by Mai Le

What is a Mandala?

The word *mandala* is the ancient Sanskrit name for circle.

A mandala is both a symbol and a tool, giving us a way to see the world and to look at ourselves. Mandalas appear in cultures all around the world.

While the mandala's design may be dominated by squares or triangles, it most often takes the shape of a concentric pattern emanating from the circle's center. Tibetan sand paintings, Gothic rose windows, Indian dream catchers and ancient labyrinths are all different kinds of mandalas.

In some traditions, the mandala stands for the cosmos, and outlines a sacred space. Others see mandalas as representing the three layers of human awareness: consciousness, subconsciousness and unconsciousness.

Looking into a mandala is said to bring the viewer closer to that which we can't see or know — the infinite mystery at the center of the universe.

You may see a mandala drawn on paper, painted in sand, built from stone, woven from fiber or pieced together in glass. You could even make a mandala of beautiful vegetables arrayed in a lovely bowl.

It may be large enough to walk through, or small enough to fit inside your hand.

Wherever you see one, a mandala is there to bring you to your center. To peace.

Where It Began

A well-known Buddhist proverb states, *"When the student is ready, the teacher appears."* My "teacher" was a simple blue bowl I found at a garage sale. Of course, I didn't know it at the time.

The time was the 1980's, an especially difficult time for me and my colleagues in the health professions. The AIDS crisis was erupting and we all felt its impact. The stories were heartbreaking. And there was so little that any of us could do.

One afternoon, in need of some spiritual uplift, I took a trip to the de Young Museum, where some Tibetan Buddhist monks would be creating a sand mandala.

Hunched on their knees around a bright blue board, sitting head to head and not speaking a word, the four monks worked in perfect harmony. The intricacy of the design they created on the wooden palette was incredible. Every grain of sand was perfectly placed.

The mandala would take the monks almost a week to complete. As a reminder of life's impermanent nature, they would destroy it soon after they were through.

I didn't want to witness that part.

In the fall, the community started holding lunches for AIDS patients. Preparing food didn't seem like much of a contribution, but it was all I had.

I channeled every desire and intention for healing I wanted to convey and put it into making a healthy salad. I bought the best veggies I could find: Deep magenta beets. Brilliant green and bright yellow peppers. Ruddy red tomatoes. Dazzling orange

carrots. I peeled, sliced, chopped and grated everything with love and care. And I took my blue bowl to serve it in.

I took my time making the salad look as nice as I could. Deep greens on the bottom. Circles of summer squash around the rim. Sprinkles of carrots, stripes of peppers and dots of tomatoes at the center.

When it was all done, I saw something I didn't expect to see: I had created a mandala in salad. Just like the monks' sand mandala, it was sitting on a background of healing blue. And it would soon be joyously destroyed.

The vegetables were fresh but, I must admit, there was nothing extraordinary about that salad. And yet, person after person remarked to me how delicious it was. I had to believe that the love I put into it came through as they ate it.

After that first lunch, I made blue-bowled mandala salad for many other AIDS lunches. And, whenever I was invited to bring something to eat, I always brought it in the blue bowl.

I still do.

Like the background of the monks' sand mandala, my blue bowl reminds me that every action I make sits on a base of intention. When I fill the blue bowl I remember that what I put in is what others will get out.

I remember that the act of creation is celebrated in the act of destruction.

And, most importantly, the blue bowl reminds me that even things from very humble beginnings can be transformed for a higher purpose.

My blue bowl was the initial inspiration for this book. My intention is that it bring something delicious and nourishing to you.

There is a morning where presence
comes over you, and you sing ...
Your heart hears, and no longer frantic,
begins to dance.   ~ Rumi

Eating as a Spiritual Practice

Good food is one of life's great gifts. A beautiful meal engages all of our senses. Smell. Sight. Taste. Touch. And yes, even sound. What would a wonderful crisp apple be without its snap?

Unfortunately, for many of us, food has slipped from a sensory pleasure into a check-off chore. As a society, we have decided that expedience and convenience are more important than contentment.

In our hyper-scheduled, always-on world, it's hard *not* to eat and run. And it's hard to feel satisfied when the only reason you're sure you ate is because you have an empty wrapper in your hand.

Maybe you do take time to eat, but you're realizing that your favorite "comfort" foods are turning into "discomfort" foods. Instead of revving up your morning, your usual 7 am muffin and coffee make you want to nap before lunch. And the pasta you always loved leaves you with a stomachache after dinner.

What's going on? It's not just you, and it's not only our schedules.

Technology has given us ample food, perfectly packaged, pasteurized products and beautifully unblemished produce. But there's one big problem: a lot of us can't digest it.

What to do?

Have courage. Acknowledge what's true for you.

Have patience. Take time to discover what may be a new way of eating.

Have fun! Experiment. This can be a delicious journey!

Let's get started!

We are living in a world today where lemonade is made from artificial flavors and furniture polish is made from real lemons.
~ Alfred E. Newman

Take Stock

Whatever your relationship with food now, it is possible to rediscover, or discover for the first time, how to eat and feel well fed physically and emotionally.

Start noticing how you feel about *what* you eat, how you feel *when* you eat, and *how* you feel after you eat.

Do you hear yourself saying things like:

• I don't know what to eat anymore.
• All the fun/joy has gone out of eating.
• There's nothing I can eat.
• I don't have time to eat.
• I'm just going to grab something.
• Nothing agrees with me.
• It doesn't matter what I eat, I always feel tired/hungry.

Those phrases are clear indications that it's time for you to take stock of your relationship with food.

If you feel that you're being deprived or restricted or are suffering from what you can and cannot eat, your ideas *about* eating may be getting in the way of enjoying *what* you are eating.

It may be true that you can't eat some of the things you love. It is also true that there are still many ways you can delight both your palette and be at peace with your body.

To find out the best path to follow, you first need to know where you stand now.

Take stock of your relationship with food.

- **Write down your beliefs (positive and negative) about what you can and cannot eat. For example:**

  > I love red peppers, but I can't digest them.
  > Everything I eat makes me fat.
  > I can't get started without my morning coffee.
  > I could eat the same thing every day.
  > I need to start my morning with a diet soda.

- **Make a list of things you love to eat.**

- **Keep a food journal.** We've included some food journal pages at the back of the book (pages 102 to 109) to help get you started. You can use those pages, copy more or start a separate food journal.

For a week, track:

  - The time you eat.

  - How you felt when you started to eat.
    (Hungry/Starved/Shaking/Foggy/etc.)

  - What you ate.

  - How you felt after you ate.
    (Tired/Energized/Satisfied/Still Hungry/etc.)

- **After a week, take a look at your journal.**

Are you eating the foods you love? Do you love them when you eat them? Do you notice certain patterns after eating particular foods? Did anything about what or when you eat surprise you?

Becoming aware of how you feel before and after you eat is a great way to begin developing a more nourishing relationship with food, and will help you begin to see the connection between what you eat and how you feel.

Be Present

Just a few generations ago, people worked in order to eat. Dinner was our reward for a day of hard work. Today, we eat in order to work. We eat in the car, at our desks, while on the phone. We schedule important activities, then fit meals in where we can.

It's easy to eat and do something else, but it's hard to maintain awareness of how much and what your body needs if you're not paying attention.

Giving yourself the time you need to appreciate and digest your meal can have a profound effect on how you feel.

Even if you don't think you can afford the luxury of extended meal times, here are some ways you can be more present while eating:

• **Give yourself time to eat.** Literally schedule time on your calendar that you will spend eating. It may be fifteen minutes. It may be an hour. Use all of that time for eating.

- **Take a moment to arrive before you eat.** Before you start eating, take time to register how you feel physically and emotionally. How hungry are you? Are you still thinking about a conversation from earlier in the day? Worrying about what's coming up next? To the best of your ability, let those things go, so you can enjoy the food in front of you.

- **Really look at what you're eating.** Take a minute to see what's on your plate. (Do you have your food on a plate?) How does it look to you? Is it visually appealing? Does it smell good? Is it what you want to eat?

- **Eat without distraction.** Turn off your phone, computer, TV, any other electronic devices you carry. Don't read while you're eating. For the time you have, simply focus on your food.

- **Be aware of what you're eating**. You're probably aware of tasting the first bite, or maybe even the first few. After that, it's easy to move into the automatic eating zone. See how long you can keep tasting your food. When you're present to what you're eating, you may find that it takes less food to feel satisfied.

- **Chew slowly.** Make sure you've finished one bite before beginning the next. Put your fork down while you chew.

- **Be aware of how your body is reacting to your food.** If something doesn't agree with your system, your body is probably giving you clues while you're eating. You know that if you eat hot, spicy peppers your tongue burns and your eyes water. If you have a food sensitivity, such as to wheat or grain, the responses may be more subtle. If your stomach starts making noises or you begin to feel itchy, tired or headachey while you're eating, stop. The more you listen to your body, the easier it will be for you to understand what is right for you.

- **Be aware of when you've had enough.** When you take time to be aware of what you're eating, you can also recognize when you've had enough. On Japan's Okinawa island, whose men and women are among the healthiest and longest lived in the world, people follow the practice of *hara hachi bu* — eating only till 80% full. With our supersized portions, many of us in the United States continue eating long after we know we've had enough.

The simple practice of building awareness is a very good place to begin creating a more connected relationship with what you eat.

Taste

Think of something you absolutely will not eat. You probably tried it once, and decided that was enough. What was it? Was the texture unpleasant? Too bitter? Too sour?

Even if the first (and last) time you ate something was a very long time ago, you probably have a vivid memory of your reaction to it. Maybe you didn't care for the way it smelled. Or the way it felt in your mouth. Maybe you just couldn't look at it. Whatever the reason, that memory was powerful enough to keep you from ever trying it again.

Now think of something you love to eat. Something you eat routinely, or have eaten many more times than you could possibly recall. Can you remember what it tastes like? Do you have an incredibly powerful positive reaction when you think of it? Probably not. The better we know something and the more we feel comfortable with it, the less we notice it. The first time you taste a delicious new dish, it's a revelation. You take time to savor it. You want to experience it fully. The next time you have it, it's good, but you knew what to expect. The thrill of discovery is gone.

The more familiar we are with what we're eating, the less we really taste it. We already know we like it; therefore, we stop experiencing the taste of it as we eat. Instead of eating consciously and pleasurably, we eat mindlessly and mechanically.

To awaken our taste buds, and keep our sensitivity alive, processed food manufacturers add copious amounts of sugar and salt to every food they make. Their aim is to give us the sensation of eating something deliciously sweet, or satisfyingly salty.

As a result, the average American consumes twice the recommended maximum intake of sodium and an extra 460 sugar calories in their food every day.

To have food nourish us at a deep level, we have to get back to a place where we can actually taste what we are eating.

Here are some ways to increase your awareness and reawaken your taste buds:

- **Eat with a beginner's mind.** Look at everything you eat as if you had never seen or eaten it before. Would you choose it if you didn't already know what it tasted like? Look for things you've never tried. Be curious. Allow yourself the gift of trying something new.

- **Eliminate all packaged, processed and prepared foods for a few days.** Then, sample something you are used to eating. You will be shocked at how sweet and/or salty it tastes.

- **Spend some time getting reacquainted with familiar food friends.** Choose an organic or locally grown fruit or vegetable that you know you like to eat. Make sure it is fresh, ripe and ready. Use all your senses to experience it. Spend some time just looking at it. Look at the color, the shape, the design of it. Hold it in your hands and examine its texture. Is it rough? Smooth? Is it heavier than it looks? Does it have a noticeable fragrance? This is a fun experiment to do with others. Invite several people to the table and share what you notice.

- **Eat in hyper-slow motion**. After taking time to familiarize yourself with what you are about to eat, take a very small bite. Go slowly enough so that you can capture every moment of the experience. Think about what you're tasting.

- **Try eating in silence.** Eating, like sleeping, is a restorative act. The decision to eat in silence means you are giving yourself, and others at the table, permission to experience the full benefit of what food has to offer. When you give your full attention to what you're eating, you naturally become more discriminating about what you choose to eat.

If you'd like to get more in-depth information about gluten sensitivity, find out about being tested, or just get some help in adjusting to a gluten-free life, my website, **serenitychiro.com,** can be of great help.

Setting a Sacred Space

When we have a special gift to give we wrap it in paper and tie it with ribbon. When the artist completes a canvas she places it in a carefully chosen frame. All around the world, when people want to worship they visit, or create, a separate special place in which to do it.

In its own way, each of these actions helps to take something from the everyday world and set it apart. An object becomes a treasure. Strokes on canvas become a work of art. Thoughts and words become prayers.

In the same way, setting the space and the place in which we eat can transform our experience. When awareness and artistry are brought to the table, meals become an opportunity to reconnect with Nature, ourselves and each other.

A friend of mine used to joke that she was going to open a restaurant exclusively for singles: There would be no tables or chairs, just row upon row of kitchen sinks and countertops, so her patrons could stand up next to the sink when they ate — the same way they would at home.

We've become a culture where stopping to eat is a lot like stopping to get gas: We do it as infrequently and as quickly as possible. Dashing in and out may be fine for cars but, for people, food should be more than just fuel and eating more than just filling up.

Setting a "sacred space" doesn't have to take a lot of time or space. It simply means allowing yourself to break fully away from what you were doing previously and step into the place where you are ready, willing and able to be deeply nourished.

Here are some steps you can take to begin your journey:

• **Set your intention.** Entering a beautiful cathedral or holy temple may put you in a prayerful mood, but it is your focused intention that gives your everyday thoughts a higher purpose. Similarly, sitting at a beautiful table can certainly help in elevating your eating experience. But the most important element in setting your sacred space is the intention and attention you bring. Close your eyes, take a deep breath, arrive fully in the present and appreciate what you are about to eat. You can create a small bubble of peace wherever you are.

- **Clear a space.** Honor yourself, the food and the multiple energies and efforts that went into creating your meal by giving it, and yourself, room to breathe. Create a space dedicated to offering and accepting the beautiful food you are serving. The place where you eat may be used for multiple purposes but, before you sit down, make sure it is cleared for the sole purpose of eating. Dining tables are rarely used only for dining, but if it doesn't relate to the meal, take it off the table.

- **Remove distractions.** Avoid the temptation to chat, text, or check your e-mail, scores or stocks by turning off your devices, and putting them out of sight while you eat. Make it your intention to be fully present with your food, even if you are by yourself.

- **Set the table.** A beautiful table sets the mood for a wonderful meal, so create a space that is visually appealing. It doesn't have to be fancy or expensive. Your beautiful dishes and silverware may be a collection of pieces you've found here and there, assembled in a delightful way. As you're putting the table together, think about what you'll be eating. Choose the plates that allow your meal to shine.

- **Add special/ceremonial objects.** Ceremonial objects are an important part of what makes a space sacred. Your relationship to what's on the table, more than the pieces themselves, is what creates a sense of sacredness. Items chosen from nature — a graceful branch, a collection of leaves or smooth stones — can be lovely additions to your table. A special piece that usually sits on a shelf brings its story and meaning to your meal when you use it for a centerpiece. Look around where you are, and see what has meaning for you now.

We Feed Each Other

An ancient Chinese parable, retold in variations in many cultures, tells of an old man facing death. He wanted to know what might be in store for him on the other side.

He visited a wise man in his village to ask what Heaven and Hell were like.

The wise man led him down a strange path, deep into the countryside, where they came upon a large house.

Inside they found lots of people and many enormous tables with an incredible array of food. Then the old man noticed a strange thing: The people, all thin and hungry, were holding chopsticks twelve feet long.

They tried to feed themselves but of course could not get the food to their mouths with such long chopsticks.

The old man then said to the wise man, "Now that I know what Hell looks like, will you please show me what Heaven looks like?"

The wise man led him down the same path a little further until they came upon another large house almost identical to the first. They went inside and saw many people well fed and happy; they too had chopsticks 12 feet long.

This puzzled the old man and he asked, "I see all of these people have twelve-foot chopsticks too, yet they are well fed and happy. Please explain this to me."

The wise man replied, "In Heaven, we feed each other."

www.wisdomcommons.org

Offering Thanks

In our world of overwhelming abundance, with shelves and bins brimming over with more choices than we have time or interest to consider, it is easy to take food for granted. Food is everywhere.

Taking a moment before we eat to remember and appreciate the fact that our food didn't arrive as "manna" from heaven, but through the efforts of many, allows us to experience the extraordinary bounty of our blessing.

In thinking of our mandala salad, we appreciate the food itself, the effort and thought that went into preparing the meal, and go even deeper to set the intention that it fuel our bodies in the best and highest way possible.

Your prayer may come from your religious or cultural tradition. It may be words you are inspired to say in the moment. Or it may be a silent, short acknowledgement for the food you are about to enjoy.

Whatever words you use, and whatever form they take, offering thanks is a simple and powerful way to transform your meal from an everyday experience into a spiritual one.

Some graces and prayers of thanks from a variety of traditions are offered on the following pages. See which one calls to you — or use them as inspiration to create your own.

Photo by Susanne von Schroeder

Many Blessings

Around the world, people say it differently but with similar intention: to give thanks for food. Here is a selection of graces from many traditions and cultures.

In this food I see clearly
the presence of the entire universe
supporting my existence.

All living beings are struggling
for life. May they all have enough food
to eat today.

The plate is filled with food.
I am aware that each morsel
is the fruit
of much hard work
by those who produced it.

from the Buddhist tradition[1]

God, make us truly grateful for what we are
about to receive. May we nourish your world
as you nourish our bodies.

from the Christian tradition[2]

May it please the supreme and divine Goodness
to give us all abundant grace ever to know its
most holy will and perfectly to fulfill it.

St. Ignatius of Loyola [3]

Be praised, my Lord, through our sister, Mother
Earth, who feeds us and rules us, and produces
various fruits with colored flowers and herbs.

St. Francis of Assisi [4]

Mighty God, Father of all, Compassionate God,
Mother of all, bless every person I have met,
every face I have seen, every voice I have heard,
especially those most dear; bless every city, town,
and street that I have known, bless every sight I
have seen, every sound I have heard, every object
I have touched. In some mysterious way these have
all fashioned my life; all that I am, I have received.
Great God, bless the world.

John J. Morris, S.J. [5]

The act of offering is God (*Brahma*), the oblation is God,
By God it is offered into the fire of God,
God is that which is to be attained by him
who sees God in all.

Vishwa Dharma kee Jai
Before eating this food, we must think about the
purpose for this body's protection and nourishment.
O *Parmeshwara*, we have one prayer that we always offer
at your feet. Let my body, mind, and wealth be in the
service of Universal Dharma.

from the Hindu tradition [6]

In the name of Allah, most Gracious, Most Merciful.

from the Islamic tradition [7]

Blessed are You, O Lord, our God, King of the Universe,
Creator of the fruit of the earth
(*pri ha-adama*)/the fruit of the vine (*pri ha-gafen*)/
the fruit of the tree (*pri ha-etz*).

Blessed are You, Lord, our God, King of the
Universe, who creates varieties of nourishment.

from the Jewish tradition [8]

Creator, Earth Mother, we thank you
for our lives and this beautiful day.
Thank you for the bright sun and the rain we
received last night. Thank you for this circle
of friends and the opportunity to be together.
We want to thank you, especially at this time
for the giveaway of their lives made by the
chicken, beets, carrots, grains and lettuce.
We thank them for giving their lives, so we may
continue our lives through this great blessing.
Please help us honor them
through how we live our lives.

from the Native American tradition [9]

May the food we are eating make us aware of the
inter-connections between the universe and us, the earth
and us, and all other living species and us. Because each
bit contains in itself the life of the sun and the earth,
may we see the meaning and value of life from
these precious morsels of food.

Thich Nhat Hanh [10]

What's Right for You

We have managed to talk about everything except the most important thing: What do you want to eat?

It's a simple enough question. One that we probably ask ourselves and others several times a day. But figuring out *what* to eat, what we *want* to eat and what we *can* and *cannot* eat has become a major issue for many of us.

We haven't suddenly become a nation of fussy eaters by choice. As a population, we're having an increasingly hard time digesting our food. We are developing food intolerances and sensitivities as never before.

Gluten, especially, is causing a lot of us a lot of problems. Gluten is the protein that gives certain grains their elastic, chewy texture.

Currently, 1 in 100 people has the most extreme form of gluten sensitivity, celiac disease, marked by severe gastrointestinal symptoms. For every gluten-sensitive person with GI symptoms, there are 8 others who are GI-symptom free but are experiencing issues elsewhere in their bodies. Their gluten sensitivity may be triggering problems in their brain or nervous system, thyroid, heart, skin, muscles or joints.

An additional 10% of the population has gluten sensitivity in the latent form. Their symptoms are slowly developing and may not be evident for many years.

What's going on? We are allergic to gluten! And with it increasingly used as an additive or extender in many packaged foods, we are more exposed to it than ever before.

When an allergic person eats gluten, the gut becomes inflamed. Eventually, the inflammation becomes so severe that the gut loses its ability to function. That leads to an extremely broad spectrum of issues, which can affect the entire body.

In addition to the gut, gluten sensitivity can affect the thyroid, brain, skin, muscles and nerves. If that sounds like just about everything, it kind of is. Women are three times more likely than men to be affected; people who have relatives with gluten sensitivity or an autoimmune disease are also more likely to be sensitive themselves.

One more thing it's important to know: Gluten isn't just in wheat. It's also in rye, barley, kamut and spelt. And once you start reading labels, you'll be amazed at how many foods have gluten additives.

Is there any good news? Yes! Contrary to what many people are told, oats do not contain gluten. (They come from a different branch of the grain family tree.) You do need to be a little careful, though, because many oats are grown and/or processed near wheat products and easily become contaminated. If you are gluten sensitive and want to eat oats, look for a package that is marked "gluten free."

So, how do you know if gluten is creating trouble for you?

A good way to start is simply to keep a food journal and notice how you feel before and after eating. If you feel okay before a meal, and notice your stomach hurts, your head aches or you feel light headed, dizzy, or otherwise uncomfortable afterwards, take a look at what you had to eat.

You could also try eliminating gluten from your diet for a week or two and see if you feel better. This might seem like a radical and difficult thing to do, but when you start feeling better it will feel natural and easy.

Choosing foods that agree with your system will make a huge difference in how you feel about food, and how you feel overall.

Barn's burnt down ... now I can see the moon.
~ Masahide, Japanese poet

Let the beauty we love be what we do. There are
hundreds of ways to kneel and kiss the ground.
~ Rumi

Eat Joyfully

When people find out that they are gluten sensitive, they frequently go into something of a mourning period, thinking of all the things they love that they will no longer be able to eat.

Food is certainly an important part of what comes to the table. But when you can celebrate and enjoy what else you bring — intentions, feelings, friends — it's easier to appreciate all you have instead of focusing on what has been "lost."

The truth is that there is no reason to mourn at all. Good-tasting gluten-free alternatives for every kind of food are available today. And more are coming to the market all the time. E-mail me at glutenfreelist@serenitychiro.com and I will be happy to send you my personal shopping list of favorite gluten-free staples.

You may also find, as I did, that the necessity to be gluten free provides inspiration to try new things in the kitchen. When you have to find a new way of doing things, you just may find you like the new way better. That's what happened to me. And that's where all of these recipes came from: my kitchen.

All of these recipes have been kitchen- and guest-tested on multiple occasions, and have received glowing reviews. Simple and straightforward, even an inexperienced cook will be able to follow them and create a delicious, healthy meal quickly and easily.

You have both my permission and encouragement to test, tweak and modify any of these recipes to suit your taste. Spice them up, take an idea and run with it. Try something cold that's hot, or hot that's cold.

Whatever you do, eat with joy — and enjoy eating!

Recipes – Eat Joyfully

 Gluten-free

 Vegetarian

 Vegan

Breakfast

Strawberry Smoothie

Basic Ingredients:
    8 oz. Almond milk
        Or 8 oz. Rice milk
        Or Yogurt (coconut or almond)
    6 oz. Fresh or frozen strawberries
    1 Scoop rice protein powder (several varieties available):
        A. Type for blood sugar balancing or
        B. Type used to reduce inflammation or
        C. Type used for detoxification
        D. Type used for cardiovascular support

Optional Ingredients:
    ½ to 1 Medium banana (not too ripe)
    2 oz. Blueberries or raspberries
    or other fruit of your choice

Nutritional Supplements (also optional):
    2 Drops liquid vitamin D_3°
    1-2 t. EPA/DHA liquid°
    1 Scoop powdered glucosamine°
    ½-1 Scoop multivitamin powder
    ½ t. Powdered probiotics
    1 t. CoQ10 liquid
    1 Scoop dehydrated fruit/veggies
    1 Scoop dehydrated veggies (greens)

Always choose organic fruit whenever possible.

Put all selected ingredients in blender.

Mix for approximately 15 seconds or until smooth.

Usually the natural sweetness of the fruit is sufficient for great flavor. If additional sweetness is desired add 1 t. of raw organic agave nectar or raw organic honey.

Makes one serving when used as meal replacement.

°Ingredients are not vegetarian or vegan.

Mixed Fruit Smoothie

Basic Ingredients:

8 oz. Almond milk

Or 8 oz. Rice milk

Or Yogurt (coconut or almond)

choose 2 fruits
½ to 1 Medium banana (not too ripe)
2-4 oz. Fresh or frozen pineapple
2-4 oz. Fresh or frozen mango
2-4 oz. Fresh or frozen strawberries
2 oz. Fresh or frozen raspberries, blackberries, blueberries or cherries
1 Medium Fuji apple, cored

1 Scoop rice protein powder (several varieties available):

A. Type for blood sugar balancing or

B. Type used to reduce inflammation or

C. Type used for detoxification or

D. Type used for cardiovascular support

Nutritional Supplements (also optional):

2 Drops vitamin D_3°

1-2 t. EPA/DHA liquid°

1 Scoop powdered glucosamine°

½-1 Scoop multivitamin powder

½ t. Powdered probiotics

1 t. CoQ10 liquid

1 Scoop dehydrated fruit/veggies

1 Scoop dehydrated veggies (greens)

Always choose organic fruit whenever possible.

Choose fruit in season, choose fruit that you love! Put all selected ingredients in blender.

Mix for approximately 15 seconds or until smooth.

Usually the natural sweetness of the fruit is sufficient for great flavor. If additional sweetness is desired add 1 t. of raw organic agave nectar or raw organic honey.

Makes one serving when used as meal replacement.

°Ingredients are not vegetarian

Mixed Berry Delight Smoothie

Basic Ingredients:

8 oz. Almond milk

Or 8 oz. Rice milk

Or Yogurt (coconut or almond)

choose 2 fruits
2-4 oz. Fresh or frozen raspberries
2-4 oz. Fresh or frozen blackberries
2-4 oz. Fresh or frozen blueberries

Optional Ingredients:

½ to 1 Medium banana (not too ripe)

2-4 oz. Cherries or plums

other fruit of your choice

1 Scoop rice protein powder (several varieties available):

A. Type for blood sugar balancing or

B. Type used to reduce inflammation or

C. Type used for detoxification or

D. Type used for cardiovascular support

Nutritional Supplements (also optional):

2 Drops vitamin D_3°

1-2 t. EPA/DHA liquid°

1 Scoop powdered glucosamine°

½-1 Scoop multivitamin powder

½ t. Powdered probiotics

1 t. CoQ10 liquid

1 Scoop dehydrated fruit/veggies

1 Scoop dehydrated veggies (greens)

Always choose organic fruit whenever possible.

Put all selected ingredients in blender.

Mix for approximately 15 seconds or until smooth.

Usually the natural sweetness of the fruit is sufficient for great flavor.

If additional sweetness is desired add 1 t. of raw organic agave nectar or raw organic honey.

Makes one serving when used as meal replacement.

°Ingredients are not vegetarian

South Seas Island Smoothie

Basic Ingredients:

8 oz. Almond milk

Or 8 oz. Rice milk

Or Yogurt (coconut or almond)

choose 2 fruits

4-6 oz. Fresh or frozen pineapple

4-6 oz. Fresh or frozen mango

4-6 oz. Fresh, ripe papaya, seeded and peeled

4-6 Fresh lychee fruit, peeled and seeded if available

Optional Ingredients:

½ to 1 Medium banana (not too ripe)

Other fruit of your choice

1 Scoop rice protein powder (several varieties available):

A. Type for blood sugar balancing or

B. Type used to reduce inflammation or

C. Type used for detoxification or

D. Type used for cardiovascular support

Nutritional Supplements (also optional):

2 Drops vitamin D_3°

1-2 t. EPA/DHA liquid°

1 Scoop powdered glucosamine°

½-1 Scoop multivitamin powder

½ t. Powdered probiotics

1 t. CoQ10 liquid

1 Scoop dehydrated fruit/veggies

1 Scoop dehydrated veggies (greens)

Always choose organic fruit whenever possible.

Put all selected ingredients in blender and blend for approximately 15 seconds or until thoroughly blended.

Usually the natural sweetness of the fruit is sufficient for great flavor. If additional sweetness is desired add 1 t. of raw organic agave nectar or raw organic honey.

Makes one serving when used as meal replacement.

°Ingredients are not vegetarian

Chocolate Protein Smoothie

Basic Ingredients:

8 oz. Almond or rice milk (unsweetened), chocolate, original, or vanilla

½ to 1 Medium banana (not too ripe)

In addition to the banana, you may add 2 oz. blueberries, raspberries or other fruit of your choice

1 Scoop chocolate protein powder:

A. Type for blood sugar balancing or

B. Type for cardiovascular support or

C. Vegan type for detoxification

D. Type used for cardiovascular support

Nutritional supplements (also optional):

2 Drops liquid vitamin D$_3$°

1-2 t. EPA/DHA liquid°

1 Scoop powdered glucosamine°

½-1 Scoop multivitamin powder

½ T. Powdered probiotics

1 T. CoQ10 liquid

1 Scoop dehydrated fruit/veggies

Always choose organic fruit whenever possible.

Put all selected ingredients in blender.

Mix for approximately 15 seconds or until smooth.

Usually the natural sweetness of the fruit is sufficient for great flavor. If additional sweetness is desired add 1 t. of raw organic agave nectar or raw organic honey.

Makes one serving when used as meal replacement.

°Ingredients are not vegetarian

Organic Nutty Granola

I love granola! I know it is typically eaten for breakfast, but sometimes I have a small amount for a snack or for dessert.

Ingredients:

8 c. Organic gluten-free oats
1 c. Organic chopped walnuts
1 c. Organic chopped almonds
Other organic nuts of your choice may be added
½ c. Organic sesame seeds
½ c. Organic sunflower seeds
¼ c. Organic flaxseed (optional)
½ c. Raw organic agave nectar or raw organic honey
½ c. Organic canola oil
1 T. Organic vanilla extract (or tasty organic almond extract)
Shredded coconut (optional)

Organic Nutty Granola continued

Get out 2-3 deep cookie sheets.

Preheat oven to 325 degrees.

Place all three liquid ingredients in a large measuring cup and stir. Place all dry ingredients in a large pot.

Pour wet ingredients into dry ingredients and stir.

Spread granola mixture evenly on cookie sheets, and put onto middle shelf of oven. (Lower shelf will be too hot.)

After about 10 minutes stir the granola so it cooks evenly.

At about 15 to 18 minutes it should be done cooking. You want to avoid browning, as this has been found to increase the aging process.

Remove from the oven and cool. When the granola is cool I refrigerate it in covered glass containers to keep it fresh.

Serve in ½-1 c. servings with your favorite milk alternative. I often use unsweetened almond milk, though others might use rice milk or coconut milk.

Note: Lots of folks add dried fruit to granola. It can add another interesting flavor. If you have a tendency to yeast (candida) overgrowth, however, it is better to avoid dried fruit.

Note: Using gluten-free oats I find it advisable to mix all ingredients and let stand for up to one hour to let the liquid soak into the oats, then bake as directed.

Makes approximately 12 one-cup servings.

Mixed Brown and Wild Rice Tabouli Salad

This is one of my favorite recipes of all time!

Mix together in a mixing bowl these ingredients:
- 2 c. Cooked *Brown or Brown and Wild Rice* recipe (p. 83)
- 2 Medium tomatoes, finely chopped (optional)
- ½ Medium onion, finely chopped
- 2 Stalks celery, finely chopped
- 3 Medium cloves garlic, finely chopped
- 3 T. Spearmint or peppermint leaves, chopped
- 6 T. Parsley, chopped
- 2 T. Sesame seeds
- 2 T. Sunflower seeds
- 3 T. Fresh lemon juice
- 3 T. Olive oil
- ¾-1 t. Sea salt, unrefined
- Dash pepper as desired

Stir all ingredients together, making sure that there is no clumping in the rice. This is a delicious combination of flavors! Of course, you may increase or decrease the quantities of the different ingredients according to your taste.

Refrigerate after preparation – tastes best several hours after preparation as the flavors begin to blend.

Serve as is or serve on organic lettuce leaves. (It's best if all ingredients are organic.)

Makes approximately four servings.

Gluten-free Quesadillas

Make gluten-free quesadillas using brown rice tortillas. I use a quesadilla maker as it is easy and heats evenly. The filling can vary as far as your imagination can take you! I will list some of the ingredients I have used on occasion:

> Leftover sautéed veggies, making sure to drain any juice
> Sliced or chopped olives
> Cut fresh or frozen corn
> Non dairy cheese
> Roasted peppers
> Sun-dried tomatoes

Place one brown rice tortilla on the maker.

Place veggies, cheese, and any filling items you desire making sure there is no liquid. I think 4-5 T. of filling is sufficient so the quesadilla filling will not leak out the sides.

Cover with a second brown rice tortilla, then close quesadilla maker for six minutes (use timer).

Use a spatula of some sort to remove the hot quesadilla, place on plate. Then, using kitchen scissors, cut along score lines on quesadilla.

Dip in salsa or guacamole if desired. Delicious!

One quesadilla (six sections) is one full-meal serving.

Lentil Soup

This soup can have many variations. The two secrets to making it delicious are having all organic and fresh ingredients (other than the dried lentils) and the seasonings, which make it very tasty and special.

Ingredients:

  2 c. Green or red lentils (this recipe can also be made with yellow split peas)
  2 Quarts filtered water
  3 Medium carrots, sliced
  3 Medium potatoes, cubed (use red or Yukon gold)
  3 Celery stalks, sliced
  1 Small onion
  2 Zucchini in thick slices (optional)
  3 Medium tomatoes, chopped (optional)
  5-6 oz. Spinach, washed (optionally, you can use swiss chard or collard greens)
  1 T. Cumin
  1 T. Coriander
  1 T. Turmeric
  1-3 t. Himalayan or unrefined sea salt (contains trace minerals)

Put all ingredients except spinach in a stainless steel pot, cover and bring to a boil.

Once boiling, turn heat to low and continue cooking for 45-50 minutes, or until lentils have softened.

At this point, add spinach, stir, and continue cooking for 3-5 minutes until spinach has wilted.

Serve by itself or with a spoonful of *Mixed Brown and Wild Rice*, (p. 83).

A very delicious, hearty, and healthy vegetarian meal!

Makes eight servings.

Yellow Split Pea Daal
(*A delicious variation of Lentil Soup recipe*, (p. 61)

Ingredients:
- 2 c. Yellow split peas
- 6-8 c. Filtered water
- 3 Medium carrots, sliced
- 3 Medium potatoes cubed (red or Yukon gold)
- 3 Celery stalks, sliced
- 1 Small onion, chopped
- 1 T. Cumin
- 1 T. Coriander
- 1 T. Turmeric
- 1-3 t. Himalayan salt

Put all the above ingredients in a stainless steel pot and bring to a boil.

Once boiling, turn heat to low and continue cooking for 45 minutes or until tender.

The daal is delicious just like this. You may optionally add any veggies you desire at this point and continue cooking for 5-10 minutes. Be creative. What do you think would taste good to add to this dish?

Makes eight servings. Enjoy!

Turkey Burgers

This recipe can be used to make turkey meatloaf as well. If you have extra, form into patties and freeze to cook later.

Ingredients:
    1 lb. Ground turkey breast, organic
    1 lb. Ground chicken thigh, organic
    2 Eggs, medium size (optional)
    4 oz. Cooked *Brown or Brown and Wild Rice* recipe (p. 83)
    (You may use millet, quinoa or amaranth as well)
    3 Large stalks celery, chopped
    2 Medium carrots, chopped
    1 t. Salt (to taste)
    1 T. Chopped parsley
    1-2 T. Non dairy cheese (as topping)

Mix all ingredients except non dairy cheese in mixing bowl.

Form into eight palm-sized patties.

Put the patties in a medium skillet.

Cook on medium heat for 4-5 minutes on each side until lightly browned. Watch over them to make sure they don't stick.

At the end of cooking, if you like, sprinkle some non dairy cheese on top, turn the heat to medium-low, place a lid on the skillet for 2 minutes and let the cheese melt on top.

Makes eight servings. Delicious!

Snacks

Baba Ganoush *(eggplant puree)*

Can be made hours ahead if kept well covered and also keeps well in the fridge. Serve at room temperature.

Ingredients:
   3 Garlic cloves (or to taste)
   1 Large eggplant
   ½ c. Tahini (sesame seed paste, to taste)
   ¼ c. Fresh lemon juice (or to taste)
   1 t. Salt (to taste)

Heat oven to 400 degrees.

Prick eggplant and bake on a cookie sheet for 30 minutes or until soft.

Cool a little, then peel outer skin, discard.

Put the garlic, eggplant, tahini and lemon juice in a clean, dry blender and whirl. Mixture should be smooth.

Taste and adjust flavors, adding more tahini if too lemony or adding more lemon if tahini is too strong.
Add salt if desired.

To serve: Spread on a plate. For gluten-free serving, use rice crackers or fresh vegetables to scoop the dip. This is very tasty!
I like to scoop the dip with unsalted sesame rice crackers.

Serves approximately four as an appetizer or snack. Enjoy!

Hummous *(garbanzo bean puree)*

Can be made hours ahead if kept well covered and also keeps well in the fridge. Serve at room temperature.

Ingredients:
  3 Garlic cloves
  15 oz. Cooked garbanzo beans (make sure they're BPA free if you're using canned)
  ½ c. Tahini (sesame seed paste)
  ¼ c. or more Fresh lemon juice (to taste)
  2 t. Cumin
  1 t. Salt (to taste)
  Sprinkle of cayenne

In a clean, dry blender whirl the garlic, beans, tahini and lemon juice. Mixture should be very smooth. Taste, and adjust the flavors of the tahini and lemon by adding one or the other so one flavor is not stronger than the other. Adding salt can also cut a lemony flavor. Add cumin and cayenne. Keep tasting throughout the process.

To serve: Spread hummous on plates. Extra virgin olive oil can be drizzled on top if desired. Garnish with a few whole garbanzo beans, parsley and a sprinkle of cayenne pepper or paprika. For gluten-free serving, use rice crackers or fresh vegetables to scoop the dip.

Serves approximately four as an appetizer or snack.

Dolmas

These are a tasty snack for just about any time, as well as a component of a delicious Mediterranean meal, which would include *Hummous* (p. 66), *Baba Ganoush* (p. 65), *Brown Rice Tabouli Salad* (p. 59) and fresh veggies.

Ingredients:

1 *Brown Rice Tabouli Salad* recipe (page 59)

Ital? 7.7 oz. Jar preserved (or fresh) grape leaves or swiss chard leaves (Fresh grape leaves or swiss chard leaves must be scalded in boiling water and cooled before use)

1 T. Garlic-infused olive oil

1 T. Lemon juice (optional)

Using the *Brown Rice Tabouli Salad* as a filler, we can create dolmas or stuffed grape leaves. Use one jar preserved grape leaves, fresh grape leaves, or swiss chard leaves.

Rinse and pat dry the preserved leaves to remove salt.

Place a leaf with the stem toward you, placing approximately 1 T. of the mixture in the center of the leaf toward the bottom.

Fold in the sides and roll the leaf away from you.

When complete, repeat this process with another leaf until you have used all the mixture.

Use 1 t. of the olive oil to coat the baking pan.

Place dolmas in rows in the bottom of the pan.

Cover and bake in a 350 degree oven for 45 minutes.

When done, you may drizzle with olive oil and lemon juice as you like. Will keep approximately one week in the refrigerator. (Leaving out tomatoes will help dolmas stay good longer.)

Serves six.

Nut Butter Fudge

Combine:

2 c. Nut butter
(I often combine several types of nut butter, such as cashew, almond, walnut, sesame or peanut.) Also, nut butter should be raw and unsalted if possible. Some folks love peanut butter so much they use entirely peanut butter.

2 T. Raw organic agave nectar or raw organic honey
4 Scoops rice protein powder
Optional: 1 t. Lemon or orange zest for extra flavor

You may use more or less of each ingredient to taste.

Mix with a spatula in a mixing bowl until all ingredients are fully blended. (If mixture is not solid enough add more protein powder.) Press into a 9" square or round baking pan.

Chill and cut into squares. You may put a walnut half on each square if you desire.

A 1" square makes a healthy between-meal snack. Delicious!

Keep unused portion refrigerated.

Makes approximately 20 one inch squares.

Gluten-free Snacks/Appetizers

Always buy organic ingredients if available – they are most nutritious. A delicious and nutritious snack is brown rice crackers dipped in a nut butter. For instance, you could try peanut butter, or cashew, walnut, almond, pecan, macadamia or other nut butters. This is a good in-between meal snack or appetizer.

There are many different flavors of brown rice crackers; some are organic, some unsalted. For purposes of being gluten free stay away from those with tamari as most tamari contains wheat and possibly barley. Even the wheat-free tamari contains a bit of barley, which contains gluten.

You could also dip sliced carrot, celery or zucchini into a nut butter for variety.

And, instead of nut butter you could use *Hummous* (garbanzo bean p. 66) or *Baba Ganoush* (eggplant p. 65) and dip either crackers, veggies or both.

One more choice for a gluten-free snack would be to dip corn chips in either guacamole or salsa.

Dinner

Mandala Salad

In this salad, we make an edible form of artwork. I've listed the veggies
I like to put in my salads. Feel free to add your favorites. To the best
of your ability all ingredients should all be fresh and organic. If you
choose canned vegetables, check to see that the packaging is BPA
free; and be sure to rinse before putting them in the salad.

define

Mandala Salad (continued)

Ingredients:
  1 lb. Spinach, washed and patted dry (or your choice of lettuce)
  1 Can cooked organic garbanzo beans, washed
  1 Can cooked organic kidney beans, washed
  1-2 c. Organic corn, fresh or frozen and thawed
  1-2 c. Organic zucchini, grated
  1-2 c. Organic beets, sliced, steamed and chilled, may be red or golden
  1-2 c. Organic carrots, grated
  Olives of your choice
  Marinated mushrooms
  Marinated artichoke hearts
  Sun-dried tomatoes in olive oil
  1-2 Ripe organic avocados, peeled, halve, remove seed and make thin slices lengthwise that can be fanned out on top of the salad
  2-3 Hard-boiled organic eggs, sliced thinly° (optional)

In a large salad bowl, arrange the spinach and/or lettuce in the bottom of the bowl – be sure it is dry or nearly dry so that the salad will last if some is left over. This is where the mandala part comes in. Let your inner artist decide how to arrange the colorful ingredients on top of the spinach/lettuce in the bowl. This can be quite a joyous experience, putting dabs of the different colored ingredients in different areas of the bowl. I tend to put certain colors north, south, east and west in the bowl.

Then, other ingredients will suggest themselves to you to put in diagonally, perhaps. They may be layered as it occurs to you to do so. You may want to add the ingredients in the order I have listed them here so that the avocados, eggs or tofu, and marinated ingredients are on top. When finished, you can feast your eyes on the beauty of your salad! Cover and chill until ready to serve. Serve with *Healthy Salad Dressing* recipe (p. 84).

° Ingredient is not vegetarian or vegan.

Baked Wild Salmon with Mango Salsa

Ingredients:

    1 lb. Wild salmon fillets, skinned
    1 Mango, ripe, sliced and cubed
    1 Avocado, sliced and cubed
    ¼ Onion, chopped
    1 Large garlic clove, minced
    Cilantro leaves from one bunch
    Pinch salt and pepper (optional)
    3 T. Lemon juice, freshly squeezed
    1 T. Organic olive oil

All ingredients should be organic whenever possible.

Place salmon in a ceramic baking dish with a lid.

Bake 25 minutes at 350 degrees. If the salmon still has its skin, then bake for 30 minutes.

While salmon is baking heat olive oil in a saucepan at no higher than medium heat. Sauté onion and garlic for several minutes until onion becomes translucent.

Remove from heat.

Squeeze the juice of one large or two small lemons, strain and set aside.

Trim leaves from one bunch of cilantro and set aside.

When the salmon is done cooking, remove from oven, place on plates and add topping ingredients individually.

First place sautéed onion and garlic on top of salmon.

Next, add a couple of tablespoons each of cubed avocado and mango.

Sprinkle desired amount of fresh cilantro.

Drizzle lemon juice on top, to your taste!

Makes two generous servings.

Baked Fresh Salmon with Dill

Ingredients:

    1 lb. Fresh wild salmon
    1 T. Chopped fresh dill
    1 Pinch Himalayan salt

Rinse fresh salmon fillet and, with kitchen scissors, cut in half.

Place the two pieces of salmon in an oven-proof glass baking dish that has a lid. If you notice any bones in the fillet remove them before baking.

Sprinkle a pinch of Himalayan salt on top of the salmon.

Next, sprinkle the chopped dill on top of the salmon.

Place well-fitting lid on baking dish and place in a preheated 350 degree oven.

Bake for 30 minutes.

Remove from oven and serve. Salmon will be delicious and moist. Enjoy with fresh veggies. A meal that is quick and memorable! The secret is very fresh fish, Himalayan salt and dill, and a tight-fitting lid so the fish actually steams.

Please note that your oven may differ from mine. With the salmon I buy and my oven, I have found that 30 minutes is the perfect baking time. (This assumes that you are baking the fish with the skin still attached.) I would ask you to experiment a little with this at home until you are sure of the performance of your oven. The first time you make the recipe, start checking the fish five minutes early to guarantee that you will not overcook your salmon. Once you know how your oven performs you can be more assured of a perfect outcome! Enjoy!

Serves two.

Fresh Vegan Pesto with Brown Rice Pasta

Ingredients:

Fresh basil leaves from one bunch, washed
3 Medium garlic cloves
½-¾ c. Extra virgin olive oil
¼ c. Brazil nuts
¼ c. Walnuts, almonds or pine nuts
½-¾ t. Salt (to taste)
12 oz. Package brown rice pasta

Place olive oil and garlic cloves in the blender and blend.

With kitchen scissors, clip basil leaves from stems, place leaves in blender and blend.

Add nuts and salt and blend. (You may taste to see if it needs more salt and add more if you desire.)

Bring 2 quarts water to a boil with a pinch of salt, then add brown rice pasta. Cook pasta, stirring frequently.

Pour the hot water and pasta into a colander and rinse. Meanwhile, place the fresh pesto topping in a large bowl. Then add hot pasta and toss until the pasta is evenly covered with the pesto.

It is especially important to stir the pasta when it is added to the water so it doesn't stick together. Personally, I like the pasta cooked slightly "al dente" or just a bit less cooked than the directions specify. To see how you might like it, a few minutes before it's supposed to be done cooking remove one piece of pasta with a spoon and run cool water over it. Taste and see what you think about its doneness. You may do this 2-3 times until you think it is done perfectly to your taste. If you are not sure how strong you want the pesto flavor, you may put half of the topping in at first and mix; then if you want stronger pesto flavor you may add the topping until it tastes just right to you. Any remaining pesto topping may be either refrigerated or frozen for future use. Serve immediately. Delicious! By the way, since we don't use cheese on top of the pesto dish you may want to sprinkle a pinch of Himalayan salt.

Makes approximately four servings.

Mixed Brown and Wild Rice with Vegetable Sauté and Non-dairy Cheese

For the rice, use a rice cooker and follow instructions for brown rice or use the *Brown Rice/Mixed Brown and Wild Rice* recipe (p.83).

Have the following vegetable ingredients on hand (any of these ingredients are optional if you prefer to omit, either due to allergy or personal preference):

1 t. Ginger, finely chopped
1 t. Garlic, finely chopped
1 Small onion, chopped
⅓ c. Pepper (green, red or yellow), chopped
½ c. Celery, chopped
3 Carrots, chopped
1 T. Organic canola oil or extra virgin olive oil
1 t. Sea or Himalayan salt
1 t. Parsley

½ t. Herbs (dill weed, thyme or basil) for flavor
½-1 lb. Mushrooms, sliced
3-4 Small organic zucchini and/or crookneck squash, chopped
1-2 Small tomatoes, fresh organic, chopped
1 Bunch rainbow chard (or one bunch fresh spinach)
4 oz. non-dairy cheese

Using the canola or olive oil over low to medium heat, sauté the ginger, garlic, pepper, celery and onion. Stir until the onions begin to appear translucent. Add sliced mushrooms and salt. As the mushrooms begin to be cooked, add zucchini and other squash, cut in small- to medium-size pieces. If you are using tomatoes, add them at this point.

Clean and chop the swiss chard/spinach. Chop the stems separately from the leaves. Add the chopped stems with the squash and sauté all for several minutes. Add the herbal seasonings to taste.

The last vegetable ingredient to add is the chopped chard or spinach leaves. Continue to sauté for 1-2 minutes.

When veggies are just about done cooking sprinkle non-dairy cheese on top of the veggies. Cover for 1-2 minutes leaving heat on low to melt cheese. When complete, may be served over brown rice, brown/wild rice blend, quinoa, or cooked brown rice pasta.

Serves four to six.

Stuffed Zucchini

Ingredients:

> 3 Medium-size zucchini, cut in half lengthwise, then cut in half crosswise
>
> 1 *Mixed Brown and Wild Rice with Vegetable Sauté and Non dairy Cheese recipe* (stuffing - p.75)

Use a tablespoon to scoop out the center of the twelve quarters of zucchini.

Chop this finely and include in the vegetables that are sautéed.

When the vegetables are done cooking, mix together with the cooked *Mixed Brown and Wild Rice.*

Use this stuffing to fill the twelve quartered zucchini.

Sprinkle with non dairy cheese and bake covered at 350 degrees for 30 minutes. If it is not quite done cooking, resume baking in five-minute increments until the desired consistency is reached.

You may wish to add more non dairy cheese right at the end of cooking to melt on top. It is delicious! Enjoy!

Tip: Make sure zucchini are dry before placing in baking pan.

Use a small amount of olive oil on the outside of each piece of zucchini and place that side down and fill.

As the zucchini cooks it will release a small amount of liquid; this process keeps it to a minimum.

Serves three to four.

Stuffed Mushrooms

Ingredients:

> 8 Medium to large portobello mushrooms with stems removed
>
> 1 *Mixed Brown and Wild Rice with Vegetable Sauté and Non dairy Cheese* recipe (stuffing - p.75)
>
> If there is stuffing left over, it may be served as a side dish

This recipe is similar to the Stuffed Zucchini recipe. In this case you may cut up the mushroom stems and sauté with the other veggies for the stuffing. When the veggies are done cooking, mix together with the cooked *Mixed Brown and Wild Rice.* Use this stuffing to fill the mushrooms. If there is stuffing left over, it may be served as a side dish or saved for later. A very tasty vegetarian meal!

Make sure the mushrooms are dry.

Place a small amount of olive oil on the top of each mushroom, then place that side down and stuff.

As the mushrooms cook they will release a small amount of liquid; this process keeps it to a minimum.

Cover and bake approximately 30 minutes at 350 degrees.

Insert a fork into one of the mushrooms to test if they are sufficiently cooked. If not, cover and cook five more minutes or until done to your taste.

Serves four. Enjoy!

Fresh Veggie Sauté and Brown Rice Pasta

Ingredients:
>   2 Medium to large organic heirloom tomatoes
>   1 Large organic eggplant
>   3 Medium organic zucchini
>   ½ lb. Mushrooms, organic if possible
>   ½ lb. Organic spinach
>   2-4 oz. Non dairy cheese
>   2 T. Organic extra virgin olive oil
>   2-3 Cloves organic garlic
>   1 T. Fresh basil leaves
>   2 T. Fresh parsley, chopped
>   1 t. Himalayan salt (to taste)
>   12 oz. Package organic brown rice pasta (can also use corn pasta or quinoa pasta if desired)

Place 2 T. olive oil in a large pan on low-medium heat.

Add chopped garlic, basil leaves, salt and chopped parsley and sauté lightly.

Peel and cube eggplant and add to pan, stirring occasionally.

Place lid on pan and allow eggplant to steam for a few minutes. When eggplant is beginning to soften, add mushrooms and continue to sauté.

In a few minutes when mushrooms are beginning to cook add cut-up tomatoes and sliced zucchini.

Cover pan and cook for additional 4-5 minutes.

At this time put 2 quarts of water with a pinch of salt in another pan and bring to a boil.

Add brown rice pasta, stirring constantly for first 1-2 minutes.

Cooking time is usually 10-12 minutes, stir occasionally.

At about 10 minutes start checking the pasta to see if it is done to your taste.

Fresh Veggie Sauté and Brown Rice Pasta continued

Go back to the pan with veggies, stir and place spinach on top. Replace lid for approximately two minutes.

If spinach has begun to wilt, then sprinkle non dairy cheese on top of spinach and replace lid.

In another two minutes cheese should be melted. If so, turn off heat and return to the brown rice pasta.

Test pasta for doneness.

When it is done to your taste, drain and rinse lightly.

Place in a serving bowl.

Spoon sautéed veggies on top and serve. Delicious!

I vary this dish during the course of the year depending on what fresh veggies are available. Occasionally I will add some sun-dried tomatoes in olive oil for an interesting flavor. Use your imagination and add ingredients you enjoy. Olives, perhaps?

Serves four.

Sides

Swiss Chard (or Spinach) and Garlic Potatoes

Ingredients:

1 Large bunch rainbow chard *or* 1 Large bunch fresh
spinach leaves
4-6 Medium red potatoes
1 T. Garlic-infused olive oil
2 t. Ghee* or trans-fat free non-dairy spread
1 T. Organic parsley (fresh and chopped) *or*
1 t. Organic parsley (dried)
½-1 t. Himalayan salt (to taste)

Wash, cut up and boil potatoes 15-20 minutes until tender.

In another pan place 1 T. garlic-infused olive oil, turn to medium heat.

Add 2 pinches of Himalayan salt.

Add cut-up stems of chard first, sauté for approximately 2 minutes,
then add cut-up leaves or add spinach and sauté lightly, until wilted.

Drain potatoes and place in a bowl containing 2 t. ghee and
¼-1 t. salt and parsley.

Stir until ghee or non-dairy spread is melted and ingredients
are mixed.

Add sautéed greens and stir.

This is a delicious side dish!

As always, it is best that ingredients be organic whenever possible.

Serves four to six.

*Ingredient is not vegan.

Roasted Asparagus

Ingredients:

    1 lb. Asparagus with bottom part removed.
    Wash, pat dry and spread out on a cookie sheet.

    1 t.-1 T. Extra virgin olive oil. Drizzle over the asparagus,
    rolling the asparagus in the oil. Asparagus should be very
    lightly coated in the oil.

Bake in 350 degree oven for approximately 7-10 minutes, opening the oven and stirring the asparagus every 2-3 minutes. When done, asparagus will look greener, very slightly cooked, sometimes slightly browned. Do not use a higher heat for cooking as overheating changes the beneficial properties of the olive oil.

This is delicious eaten immediately while warm. It is also quite excellent when refrigerated and can be used as a tasty, healthy, cold side dish. Sometimes I will make a double batch and eat some warm and then have some left over for a snack later in the week!

Serves six.

Brown Rice/ Mixed Brown and Wild Rice

There is an art to cooking brown rice, and practice makes perfect. I will give you a ballpark recipe and you will need to decide if you want just a little more or less water and just a little more or less cooking time. One cup of rice serves at least two people.

I really enjoy using organic products whenever possible as they are most nutritious. My recent favorite is organic short grain brown rice. I also enjoy mixed rice such as a gourmet blend of wild and whole-grain brown rice. Use a stainless steel pot.

Measure the number of cups of rice that you want to cook. Wash thoroughly. Use twice as much cold water as rice, and a pinch of sea salt or Himalayan salt for each cup of rice. Cover, and bring to a rolling boil, then turn the heat to low and set your timer for 45 minutes. When the timer rings, turn off the heat and let the rice stand for five minutes before serving.

Please note that when rice is too well done and "mushy" its glycemic index increases. So, rice, as other whole grains, is best served slightly "al dente" or firm to preserve its lower glycemic index.

Personally, I most often use a rice cooker that is calibrated for cooking brown rice. Following cooking instructions exactly leads to perfect rice each time. Another benefit of this approach is that the rice cooker will keep the rice perfect for up to 24 hours. I find the rice to be somewhat moist but never clumpy, never over- or underdone. The rice cooker will take a bit longer to cook, in my experience, often taking a little over an hour to complete cooking. For me the benefits of this method far outweigh the slightly longer cooking time.

Healthy Salad Dressing

I use the following ingredients for a delicious healthy salad dressing in a ratio of 2 parts oil to 1 part lemon juice or vinegar:

Organic canola oil or extra virgin olive oil
Fresh squeezed lemon juice or balsamic vinegar

Season with organic herbs of your choice. I like dill weed and parsley, but there are an infinite number of choices here.

Experiment to find what you personally enjoy the most. Sometimes I like cumin, coriander and a bit of turmeric together.

If you like, add a pinch of salt and pepper.

Drizzle over salad and enjoy!

Steamed Green Beans

Ingredients:

1 lb. Green beans, organic fresh

1 t. Dill, parsley or basil (optional)

1-2 t. Ghee* or trans-fat free non-dairy spread (optional)

Snip or slice off both ends of each bean. Sometimes as you cut off the end of a bean it will pull on a string along the side of the bean. In that case, pull the string off the bean.

Slice diagonally at approximately 1½-inch intervals.

In a stainless steel pot put 1 inch water in the bottom, then cover with a stainless steel steamer tray.

Place all beans on the steamer tray and cover pot.

Bring water to a boil and cook approximately 8-10 minutes or until just tender. Do not overcook. Beans should still be close to bright green in color.

Remove from heat with top off of the pot to prevent overcooking. I like the beans just as they are – delicious!

You may season to taste, adding herbs such as dill, parsley or basil and 1-2t. ghee or non-dairy spread if you like.

Refrigerate any uneaten beans; they are great for a snack later on that day or the next day!

Serves four.

*Ingredient is not vegan.

Desserts

Baked Apples or Pears

These are very healthy and quite easy gluten-free desserts.

Apples: I usually wash, dry and core the raw apples before placing into a baking dish.

On top of the raw apples I sprinkle cinnamon.

For four apples I use approximately 2 t. cinnamon.

Cover and bake at 350 degrees for approximately one hour or until a fork inserted into the apple can be withdrawn easily.

I have baked several types of apples, and my personal favorite is the Fuji variety of apple. I like to bake extra and refrigerate in individual containers so they can be taken to work as a snack or dessert the next day or two.

Pears: Wash pears and dry. I like organic Bosc pears; they're the best for baking.

Insert a knife several times into the raw pear and place in a baking dish with a lid. I usually bake two or more at a time. They can be refrigerated and served at a later time.

Bake for approximately one hour at 350 degrees or until a fork inserted into the pear can be removed easily.

When the pear is partially cooled, it may be eaten. Just push the seeds and stem to the side of your plate and enjoy!

One apple or one pear is one serving.

Carrot Cake — Gluten Free

Ingredients:

1 c. Organic canola oil
1¾ c. Real maple syrup
OR 1¼ c. Organic maple sugar
2 c. Organic carrots, grated raw

1 c. Organic pecans or walnuts, chopped
4 Eggs, beat well with oil and syrup, using an electric mixer

In a separate bowl combine:

1½ c. Organic oat flour
½ c. Organic tapioca flour
2 T. Baking powder
1 t. Baking soda

½ t. Organic ground ginger
½ t. Nutmeg
¼ t. Allspice
1 T. Organic cinnamon

Stir dry ingredients in a mixing bowl, then sift into wet ingredients a little at a time, stirring constantly using a hand mixer.

Fold in nuts and carrots, pour into two 8.5" x 6.5" oven-safe glass greased baking dishes. (Can use canola oil or ghee to grease the baking dishes).

Fill ½-¾ full. Do not overfill.

Bake at 350 degrees for 45 minutes. (Smaller baking dish will cook faster.) Insert a toothpick in the center.

When the cake is done, the toothpick will come out clean.

No frosting necessary! Delicious!

Serves eight.

Peach Dessert Smoothie

Basic Ingredients:

    8 oz. Almond milk
        Or 8 oz. Rice milk
        Or Yogurt (coconut or almond)
    2-3 Peaches, fresh or frozen
    8-16 oz. Rice, coconut or almond ice cream
    Sprinkle of cinnamon and/or nutmeg (optional)

Put all selected ingredients in blender.

Mix for approximately 15 seconds or until smooth.

Usually the natural sweetness of the fruit is sufficient for great flavor. If additional sweetness is desired add 1 t. of raw organic agave nectar or raw organic honey. (Can substitute 8 oz. fresh or frozen cherries for a cherry smoothie; leave out cinnamon and nutmeg).

Always choose organic fruit whenever possible.

Serves two.

Black and White Dessert Smoothie (with fruit)

Basic Ingredients:
> 8 oz. Almond milk
>> or 8 oz. Rice milk
>> or Yogurt (coconut or almond)
>
> 8-16 oz. Rice, coconut or almond ice cream
> 1-2 oz. Organic chocolate syrup

Add fruit as desired. For instance:
> 8 oz. Strawberries, fresh or frozen
> Or 8 oz. Peaches, fresh or frozen
> Or your choice of favorite fruit
> Garnish with a fresh mint leaf

Always choose organic fruit whenever possible.

Put all selected ingredients in blender.

Mix for approximately 15 seconds or until smooth.

Usually the natural sweetness of the fruit is sufficient for great flavor.

Delicious as a dessert or mid-afternoon snack!

Serves two.

Gluten-free Desserts

At home I often have fresh fruit for dessert, organic whenever possible. I usually have some combination of strawberries, kiwi, banana, pineapple, blueberries, papaya, apple, etc. I usually do not sweeten as the fruit is very tasty. If you do desire to sweeten a bit I suggest using a small amount (1 t.-1 T.) of raw organic agave nectar or raw organic honey. It is delicious, very neutral tasting and has a low glycemic index.

There are some tasty brands of gluten-free cookies that can be purchased. Also, there are interesting gluten-free cookie and brownie mixes that I have used and would recommend. There are several varieties of non-dairy ice cream, which are tasty. If at all possible, get one that is sweetened with agave syrup as this is more slowly metabolized. Please remember that gluten free does not mean calorie free, so these foods are to be enjoyed in moderation!

Apple Crisp

Ingredients:

4 Large Fuji apples, sliced medium to thin (you may choose your favorite apple; Fujis are my favorite. Lots of folks like to use Pippins for this dish.)

¼ c. Organic brown rice flour

¼ c. Gluten-free oat flour

1 c. Gluten-free rolled oats *See earlier*

1½ t. Cinnamon

½ t. Nutmeg

⅓ c. Organic canola oil

⅔ c. Organic sweetener (could be raw organic agave nectar, raw organic honey or maple syrup)

1 t. Ghee* or organic canola oil to grease pan

Optional:

1) Squeeze juice of ½ Meyer lemon over apples before baking.
2) Add ½ -¾ c. chopped organic walnuts.
3) Add ½ -¾ c. organic raisins (do not use if you have issues with yeast infections).

Choose a baking pan with a lid that will keep the apple juices within the dish. Grease pan with either ghee or organic canola oil.

Slice apples into the bottom of the baking pan.

Mix all dry ingredients with the canola oil and sweetener.

If using lemon, this is the time to squeeze the lemon over the apples. Cover the apples with the oat mixture.

Cover with lid or with aluminum foil, bake for approximately one hour at 350 degrees or until apples are soft.

Serve warm.

For an extra treat, top with a scoop of non-dairy frozen dessert. Rice milk, coconut milk, almond milk and tofu are all great vegan substitutes for ice cream. Refrigerate any leftovers; they will be excellent the next day as well.

Serves six. Enjoy!

    *Ingredient is not vegan.

My Own Recipes

Use these pages to jot down your own recipe ideas, or keep recipes you've found in other places.

My Own Recipes – I Made This!

My Own Recipes – Love This!

My Own Recipes – Try This!

Meals to Remember

This is a meal I want to remember:

This is who shared it: _____

This is what we ate: _____

This is what we said: _____

This is how we felt: _____

This is a meal I want to remember:

This is who shared it: _____

This is what we ate: _____

This is what we said: _____

This is how we felt: _____

This is a meal I want to remember:

This is who shared it: _____

This is what we ate: _____

This is what we said: _____

This is how we felt: _____

This is a meal I want to remember:

This is who shared it: _____

This is what we ate: _____

This is what we said: _____

This is how we felt: _____

Meals to Remember

This is a meal I want to remember:

This is who shared it: _____

This is what we ate: _____

This is what we said: _____

This is how we felt: _____

This is a meal I want to remember:

This is who shared it: _____

This is what we ate: _____

This is what we said: _____

This is how we felt: _____

This is a meal I want to remember:

This is who shared it: _____

This is what we ate: _____

This is what we said: _____

This is how we felt: _____

This is a meal I want to remember:

This is who shared it: _____

This is what we ate: _____

This is what we said: _____

This is how we felt: _____

7-Day Food Journal

Day 1

Date/Time: _____

Meal: _____

Mood: _____

Food: _____

Effect: _____

Date/Time: _____

Meal: _____

Mood: _____

Food: _____

Effect: _____

Date/Time: _____

Meal: _____

Mood: _____

Food: _____

Effect: _____

7-Day Food Journal

Day 2

Date/Time: _____

Meal: _____

Mood: _____

Food: _____

Effect: _____

Date/Time: _____

Meal: _____

Mood: _____

Food: _____

Effect: _____

Date/Time: _____

Meal: _____

Mood: _____

Food: _____

Effect: _____

7-Day Food Journal

Day 3

Date/Time: _____

Meal: _____

Mood: _____

Food: _____

Effect: _____

Date/Time: _____

Meal: _____

Mood: _____

Food: _____

Effect: _____

Date/Time: _____

Meal: _____

Mood: _____

Food: _____

Effect: _____

7-Day Food Journal

Day 4

Date/Time: _____

Meal: _____

Mood: _____

Food: _____

Effect: _____

Date/Time: _____

Meal: _____

Mood: _____

Food: _____

Effect: _____

Date/Time: _____

Meal: _____

Mood: _____

Food: _____

Effect: _____

7-Day Food Journal

Day 5

Date/Time: _____

Meal: _____

Mood: _____

Food: _____

Effect: _____

Date/Time: _____

Meal: _____

Mood: _____

Food: _____

Effect: _____

Date/Time: _____

Meal: _____

Mood: _____

Food: _____

Effect: _____

7-Day Food Journal

Day 6

Date/Time: _____

Meal: _____

Mood: _____

Food: _____

Effect: _____

Date/Time: _____

Meal: _____

Mood: _____

Food: _____

Effect: _____

Date/Time: _____

Meal: _____

Mood: _____

Food: _____

Effect: _____

Photo by Susanne von Schroeder

7-Day Food Journal

Day 7

Date/Time: _____

Meal: _____

Mood: _____

Food: _____

Effect: _____

Date/Time: _____

Meal: _____

Mood: _____

Food: _____

Effect: _____

Date/Time: _____

Meal: _____

Mood: _____

Food: _____

Effect: _____

About Dr. April J. Modesti

Dr. April J. Modesti has been taking a gentle approach to healing from the start of her chiropractic career in 1980. Her focus has always been on the whole person; her aim is to help her clients feel healthy and balanced throughout their lives.

After identifying her own gluten sensitivity, Dr. Modesti began to notice similar patterns in her patients. When standard responses to their complaints of headache, lethargy and gastric distress failed to help, Dr. Modesti began suggesting that what they were eating might be the cause of their symptoms.

Most often, she was right.

She began researching issues around gluten sensitivity, and in 2006 started teaching classes on living gluten free. In the process, she has become a well-known and valued resource to an ever-expanding gluten-free community.

Dr. Modesti is a long-time resident of Redwood City, CA where she enjoys gardening and the company of her golden lab, Sugar.

Susan E. Schwartz

Susan E. Schwartz is an author, speaker and branding consultant, who is working on eating better and enjoying it more. Her first book was *Teddy Bear Philosophy: Things My Teddy Bear Taught Me About Life, Love and the Pursuit of Happiness.*

Susan lives and works in San Mateo, CA with her omnivorous dog, Bailey.

Acknowledgements

I am profoundly grateful to the many people who generously contributed their time, attention, inspiration and creativity in the creation of this book.

In particular, thanks to Janet Ghanem, who worked tirelessly in helping to construct, taste and edit the recipes. I appreciate both her skill with words and her wonderfully discriminating taste buds!

Thanks so much to Laura Palazzolo, who lends her extraordinary expertise in graphic design to all of our mutual projects. Her care and expertise in this project communicate that which is beyond words.

Overwhelming thanks to my co-author Susan Schwartz. Her facility with words is an amazing talent! I have found her to have the ability to convey complicated concepts with ease and humor. I am immensely grateful for her contribution to this book. Very simply put: Thank you for the beauty and grace in your writing!

Thank you to our copyeditor, Joanne Shwed, for her skill in editing this work. Thanks also to Lisa Miller and Jil Conway for all of their encouragement and hard work keeping the office running while we've been working on this project.

I cannot forget to thank my grandmother, Grace Modesti, for her inspiration. When I was a child, her gardening and delicious cooking instilled in me a desire to create delicious food. She is no longer on the planet, but her influence lives on!

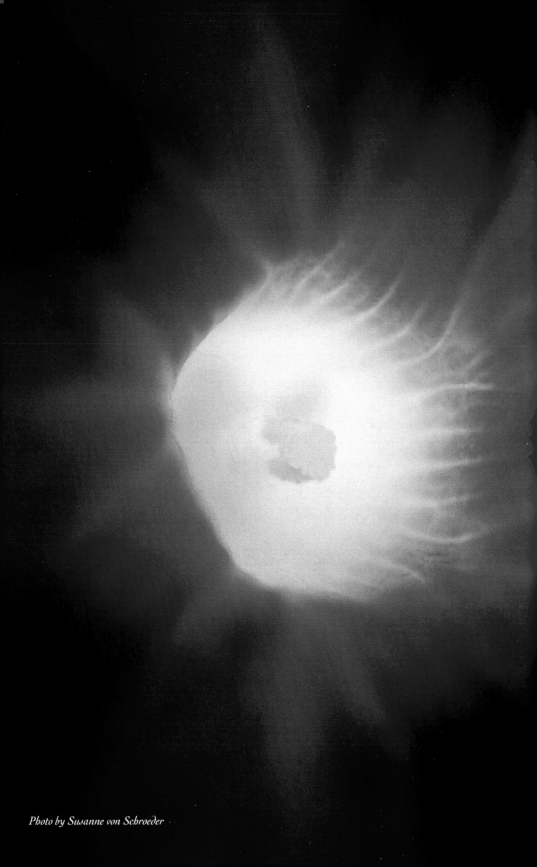

Photo by Susanne von Schroeder

Have Questions for Dr. Modesti?

Dr. Modesti is available to meet in person with patients in her Los Altos office. If you live beyond the San Francisco Bay Area, you can get an appointment with Dr. Modesti by phone.

Dr. Modesti can help guide you through all phases of gluten-free living, including:

- Testing for gluten sensitivity
- Identifying "trigger" foods in your current diet
- Identifying issues/symptoms that may be caused by gluten sensitivity
- Resolving those issues
- Creating a food program you can live with — and not feel deprived
- Recommending supplements to establish and maintain your best health

To schedule an appointment, call Dr. Modesti at 650-949-1089.

Dr. Modesti is also available to speak to groups on Gluten-Free Eating and Living. Call her office, or see her website, serenitychiro.com for more information.

May lightness, freedom and health be yours.
~ AJM

Bibliography

Grizzard, Lewis. BrainyQuote.com. Xplore Inc. (17 November 2011)
http://www.brainyquote.com/quotes/authors/l/lewis_grizzard.html

Hanh, Thich Nhat. *Call Me By My True Names* (Parallax Press, 1999).

Jensen, Bernard Ph.D. *Food Healing for Man* (Bernard Jensen, 1983).

Masahide. Zen Poetry: *Let the Spring Breeze Enter* (Grove Press, 1995).

Neuman, Alfred E. ThinkExist.com Quotations Online
http://en.thinkexist.com/quotes/Alfred_E._Neuman

Rumi, Jalal ad-Din Muhammad. *The Essential Rumi,* Harper One Translations by
Coleman Barks with John Moyne (Harper One, 2004).

http://www.wisdomcommons.org/wisbits/3241-in-heaven-we-feed-each-other

Prayers

1. Buddhist tradition:
   http://dharmarefuge.com/resources/retreat-prayers-poems

2. Christian tradition: *100 Graces: Mealtime Blessings.* Marcia M. Kelly and Jack
   Kelly (Three Rivers Press, 1997).

3. St. Ignatius of Loyola: http://ignatianspirituality.com/ignatian-prayer/prayers-
   by-st-ignatiusand-others/prayer-to-know-gods-will/

4. St. Francis of Assisi: http://conservation.catholic.org/prayers.htm

5. John J. Morris, S.J: http://St. Louis University Prayerbook and
   http://slu.edu/prayerbook/2009/12/12/mighty-god-father-of-all/

6. Hindu tradition: *The Bhagavad Gita* ,Nilgiri Press; 2nd edition 2007, 24th verse of
   the 4th chapter Chaitana Bharati, special publication 2001, Yugabda 5103

7. Islamic tradition: http://www.islamicity.com/

8. Jewish tradition: http://en.wikipedia.org/wiki/List_of_Jewish_prayers_and_blessings

9. Native American tradition: *100 Graces: Mealtime Blessings*
   Marcia M. Kelly and Jack Kelly (Three Rivers Press, 1997).

10. Hanh, Thich Nhat. Included in *A Grateful Heart: 365 Ways to Give Thanks at
    Mealtime,* M. J. Ryan, (Conari, 2011).